The Pianist's Collection

Book Eight

Beautiful music from across the centuries

Kevin Mayhew

We hope you enjoy *The Pianist's Collection Book 8*.
Further copies of this and the other books in the series are available
from your local music shop.

In case of difficulty, please contact the publisher direct:

The Sales Department
KEVIN MAYHEW LTD
Rattlesden
Bury St Edmunds
Suffolk IP30 0SZ

Phone 0449 737978
Fax 0449 737834

Front Cover: *The Cottage in a Cornfield* by John Constable (1776-1837).
Reproduced by Courtesy of the Board of Trustees of the Victoria and Albert Museum, London.

Cover designed by Juliette Clarke and Graham Johnstone.
Picture Research: Jane Rayson.

First published in Great Britain in 1992 by Kevin Mayhew Ltd.

© Copyright 1992 Kevin Mayhew Ltd.

ISBN 0 86209 287 6

Series Music Editor: Anthea Smith.

Printed and bound in Great Britain.

Contents

WALTZ IN A

Edvard Grieg (1843-1907)

TO A WILD ROSE

Edward MacDowell (1861-1908)

BAGATELLE IN G MINOR

Ludwig van Beethoven (1770-1827)

CHANSON TRISTE

Peter Ilyich Tchaikovsky (1840-1893)

INTERMEZZO

Zdenek Fibich (1850-1900)

CONSOLATION

Franz Liszt (1811-1886)

LANDLER IN A

Franz Schubert (1797-1828)

CLAIR DE LUNE

Claude Debussy (1862-1918)

23

ELEGY

Heinrich Hofmann (1842-1902)

ALLEGRETTO

Theodor Kirchner (1823-1903)

ENTRANCE

Robert Schumann (1810-1856)

MEDITATION

Felix Mendelssohn (1809-1847)

BERCEUSE

Alexander Ilynsky (1859-1920)

HUMORESKE

Stephen Heller (1813-1888)

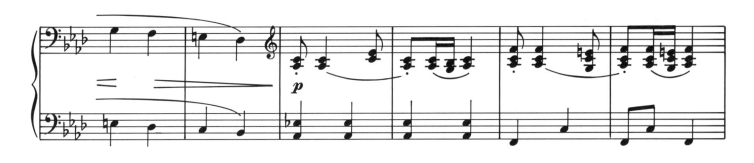

Meno mosso

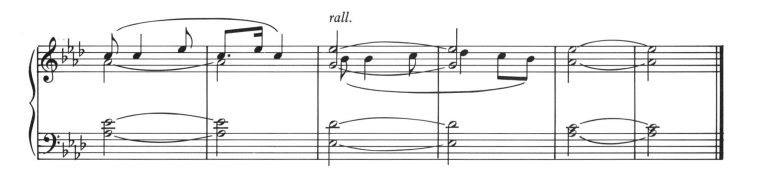

WALTZ IN E

Johannes Brahms (1833-1897)

EPILOGUE

Enrique Granados (1867-1916)

45

IMPROMPTU

Moritz Moszkowski (1854-1925)